1

POPULATIONS

1.1 Population growth

1 Population growth and population size depend on the birth rate, the death rate, time taken to reach sexual maturity, the number of offspring produced at any one time, the length of time between births, the number of individuals in a population, the length of life of individuals, migration into and out of the area.

Checks on population growth are intraspecific and interspecific competition, predation, inability to survive the environmental conditions.

2 To kill any living organisms before the culture was inoculated with the yeast.

3 To obtain the mean.

4 Graph.

5 The initial low rate of increase is the lag phase where there is cell growth as each cell increases in size with possible synthesis of enzymes and other macromolecules. The rapid increase is the logarithmic phase. Here all cells are alive and reproducing at a fairly constant rate of increase. One cell divides to give two, which give four, and so on. The final phase is the stationary phase where cells start to die and the survivors take longer to reproduce. Eventually cells die at the same rate as new cells appear. The cause may be the lack of an essential nutrient which has become exhausted, the accumulation of waste products from metabolism, or the limits of space.

6a i The rate of growth would be halved, so they would take twice as long to reach the same numbers.
ii Probably dead as the temperature is too high.
b i The same rate of growth, but the original final numbers would be about double, unless something else limited the population growth.
ii The same rate of growth, but only half the number of the original.

7 That all the individuals are effectively identical in that all are equally likely to reproduce or die at any particular time. That the rate of increase depends only on the numbers present. That the environmental conditions remain constant. For many populations, these assumptions cannot be made. Nevertheless the model remains extremely useful.

8 The turning point is between eight and ten hours. Up to then the population increase has accelerated to its most rapid rate. After that the growth rate decelerates rapidly at first (ten to twelve hours), and then more gradually and fairly uniformly to nearly zero.

9 At 6 hours where the log scale is 3.3 and the number of bacteria per cm^3 is 2000.

10 The rate of population increase starts to slow down between 8 and 12 hours. Up to 8 hours the population has doubled every hour, so that at 8 hours there are about 8000 bacteria cm^{-3}. If the population had continued doubling every hour there would have been 128 000 bacteria cm^{-3} at 12 hours. Instead, there are only 63 000.

11 For example: some algae, as in the graph; annual plants which die off after fruiting, or after a frost; insect populations with only one generation a year, or depending for their food on an annual crop.

12 The figure shows that, even with a relatively lowly organism, reproducing asexually, which has no social behaviour, and which is in a stable environment, there are high fluctuations in the population.

The initial curve shows the usual pattern, but with steps as the population remains constant for a few days and then large numbers of eggs hatch (they take only three to four days to hatch). The population increases for 20 to 40 days, then reproduction stops, some old animals die, and there is a drastic drop in the curve. The young ones then reproduce, giving a population increase.

The low points, therefore, represent an almost completely adult population, and the high points the largest number of young animals. When numbers are high, food is limiting, so growth and reproductive rates decline. The population thus picks up again when numbers are low enough for the food to go round and reproduction to restart.

1.2 Population growth under different conditions

Fig 1.5, yeast: Rate of population growth is faster when the medium is changed frequently, and the start of the stationary phase is also presumably progressively delayed. The change adds new food and removes metabolic wastes.

Fig 1.6, *Daphnia*: At the lower temperature the growth of the population is slow when compared with that at 23 °C.

Fig 1.7, Flour beetles: The amount of food is the limiting factor. The more flour, the longer the population can go on growing, until some other factor becomes limiting.

1.3 Human population

1 Figs 1.18 and 1.19.

2 The first shows the toolmaking revolution which allowed man the food-gatherer and hunter to manipulate and use a larger number of environments.

The second shows the agricultural revolution, when crops could be grown to feed a larger population than before. The third is the scientific-industrial revolution of the last 300 years.

3 Starvation, disease, intraspecific and interspecific competition, possibly attacks of parasites and predators, space or other needed resources. (Problems 1.1 and 1.6 also discuss checks to population growth.)

4 For speculation and discussion. See also the notes for question **6**.

5 For speculation and discussion. New environments could be opened up for food production and for inhabitation. The sea, for example, is the major untapped and unmanaged plant production resource on the planet. (The plants in the sea are, so far, mainly inedible.) At the moment, about one per cent of the total annual net productivity (see Problem 3.2) for the whole surface of the world, both sea and land, is needed to give everyone enough food. Could the earth perhaps have a carrying capacity about a hundred times more than the present? On the other hand, man

Fig 1.18 Estimated human world population

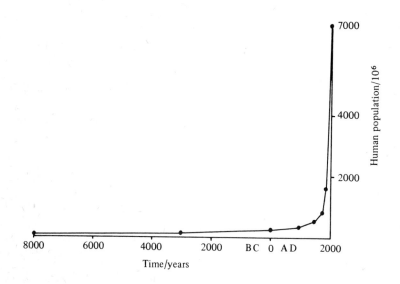

Time/years

Fig 1.19 Estimated human population plotted on a log-log scale.

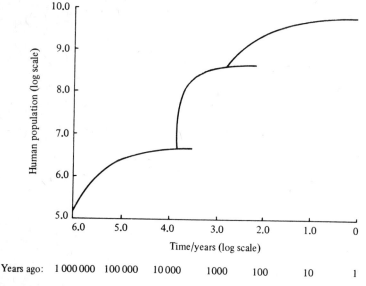

Time/years (log scale)

Years ago: 1 000 000 100 000 10 000 1000 100 10 1

is not totally a herbivore, about 10% of our food comes through a food chain with one animal in it, there are other herbivores which need a share, and about 60% to 80% of plant production is in the sea.

To go further back, most ecosystems utilize only about one to three per cent of the available energy (see Problem 3.1). The selection and management of more efficient producer communities could further increase the carrying capacity. For example, phytoplankton could be dried and powdered into a flour. There could be selection and control of other herbivores. Some, like the freshwater manatee or a large South American rodent (the capybara), unusual though they would look in a butcher's shop, feed on aquatic weeds which neither we nor our traditional farm animals will use. The eland (African antelope) grazes on land which could not be used for farming.

New foods entirely could be found, and much research is going on into the production of new types, or of food from the growth of micro-organisms on unusual substrata such as sawdust, petroleum and coal.

A completely new environment, of course, could perhaps be found on other planets or in outer space. (See also Problem 3.11.)

6 There are a number of explosive aspects to the population problem. Population, famine and malnutrition cannot be solved without tackling other problems: development, trade, urbanization, pollution, resources, energy, armaments, aid, corruption, waste, to name only a few.

The unequal distribution of food, resources, development and population across the world is a major source of potential discord. As far as population is concerned, 56.9% of the world's population lives in Asia, 11.9% in Europe, 10.1% in Africa, 8.2% in South America, 6.4% in the USSR, 6% in North America, 0.5% in Oceania. The most rapid population growth is in Africa: for 40 of the 47 areas or countries for which there are figures, the annual rate of increase is two per cent or more, ten of them having rates of three per cent or more. Twenty-six out of thirty-seven European countries have an annual rate of less than one per cent.

An increasing population needs more cities and conurbations, which lead to a greater need for energy. At the moment, the third world countries use only one twentieth of the energy used by the 'developed' nations. As the use of energy increases, so also will pollution. Some raw materials are already in short supply. Competition between countries will only make worse any hostility between them. As nuclear weapons become more widespread, will they be used by a country with a population desperate for a larger share of the world's resources? Or will there be a more reasonable share-out, resulting in a higher quality of life for many and a lower quality for some?

1.4 Populations and age

1 The age pyramid shows the reproductive ability of a population at that time. A broad base and middle in the immature and reproductive years indicate an expanding population. A top-heavy pyramid with more oldsters of post-reproductive age shows a declining population.

2 a C, b A, c B.

3 a B, b A, c C.

4 a The reduction is seen in the numbers of both sexes born between 1915 and 1920, aged between 40 and 45 years in 1960.

b The reduction is seen in those born between 1945 and 1950, aged 10 to 15 years in 1960. There was a smaller reduction during the war.

c Males aged about 18 to 40 years between 1939 and 1945 would be lost in the war (about 35 years and over in 1960). There is a large bite out of the male side here, the female numbers show a more regular pattern.

5 With increased medical care the high mortality in older age groups will decrease. Contraception, family planning and more affluence cause the birth rate to decrease.

6 a **Broad-based pyramid**: If people die while their children are still quite young,

the children have to take on adult responsibilities early. They marry and have children of their own while still young. Such a population could be fairly un-educated and may not be able to provide its own teachers, doctors and back-up services, all of whom could help to prolong the life of individuals. The relatively poor standard of living which could ensue and the lack of medical care would enable famine, pestilence or natural disaster to play havoc with the population from time to time.

b   **Top-heavy pyramid**: The average age in the second population could be twice that of the first, say 35 as opposed to 15 or so. We see a top-heavy pyramid in the UK. The birth rate has dropped for the last few years to a level now well below the previous peacetime trough of 1933. The average age of the population was 23 years in 1909. Now it is 34. By the end of the century it could be 37 or 38. People are having smaller families, at a later age than before, and old people are living longer.

In a top-heavy pyramid the educational level can be higher than in a broad-based one, as parents are alive to look after their children and become more affluent as they go up their job ladders. There are, however, problems in an ageing population. For industry, an ageing workforce means that economic growth has to follow mainly from increased individual productivity, which could be difficult. In the spending of public money, we shall need fewer schools but more cash on medical services, there will be fewer jobs for teachers but more for health visitors. In politics, there may be changes to take account of the 'grey power' which could be influential in keeping a party in office. For the workers, an increasing population of retired senior citizens imposes a heavy financial burden.

1.5   Fertility

1   For discussion. The most probable factors of those listed are disease, or rather a reduction of disease, and the length of time between births. Contraception puts an end to one baby a year as well as enabling a couple to stop at a smaller final number than in Victorian days. Live births per thousand of the population are 12.4 in the UK (21.6 in Eire, 18.2 in Spain, 9.7 in West Germany). More boys now survive than did last century, so a higher proportion of women marrying and having children may be a contributory factor to population growth. Indeed, the day may soon come when there are males surplus to (reproductive) requirements. In addition, the social climate is more favourable these days towards a woman who wants children without a husband.

Generation time is important; reproducing couples are older now than a decade or two ago, but there has been a number of fluctuations over the last hundred years around the age of starting a family. Poor nutrition a century ago may have made individuals more susceptible to disease.

2   UK: 25% of 1000 reproduce = $25 \times \frac{1000}{2} \times 2.1 = 262$ children, which gives a total population of 1262.
Other: $3 \times \frac{1000}{2} \times 4 = 600$ children which gives a total population of 1600.

3   The younger woman. Her three children will be reproducing some thirteen to eighteen years before the five children of the older woman. If those three also have their families early, the increase is compounded.

4   The increasing demand by women for better jobs and a fairer share in the responsibilities and rewards of society may cause later marriage or later child production. Delay in marriage is often due to a long education, itself due to the economic advantage to the individual of further qualifications. For some populations postponing the start of a family is more acceptable than contraception or abortion as a way of keeping the population stable. So delay caused by the demand by women for a fairer deal could slow down population growth. For a woman herself, a delay could enable her to become sufficiently secure and established in her job either to take time off and return with no penalties or to be able to afford to employ someone to look after her children while she continues working. A country with a reducing work force may, one day, find it worthwhile to provide care for small children, releasing the mother for work.

1.6   Population density and stress

1   Sexual behaviour seems to be normal as the females become pregnant. Maternal behaviour is possibly interfered with if the young are trampled on by other hamsters using the same boxes, or lactation may fail as the mothers are disrupted. The high rate of abortion or resorption suggests a hormonal imbalance in the pregnant females, possibly due to stress caused by the crowded social conditions. The death of the infants was possibly due to social disruption caused by too many animals using the same nest. There was aggressive behaviour between males, between females, and by females to males (not males to females or males to infants).

2   Use larger enclosures, provide partitions, more nesting boxes, bigger and different shaped boxes, more places to hide, burrow and escape.

1.7   Surviving

1   a 3 For example, Western man, large vertebrates.
b   1 Oysters and many other invertebrates with large numbers of small larvae which die in great numbers. Most plant species.
c   2 Most other vertebrates and some invertebrates. Animals with fairly stable populations, large enough not to notice losses by predation.

2   Medical advances, nutrition, hygiene and sanitation for a start.

3   Graphs.

4   The more widely spaced population in the unmanaged area (B).

5   Hunting in the managed area, intraspecific competition between individuals of the deer population, predation as there was less cover for the deer.

1.8   Survival in mountain sheep

1   b 3

2   The first year. 199 die before one year of age. Parental care ends at about six months. Nearly all animals who look after their young have a high mortality rate at the end of parental care. In addition, the very young animals will not be expert at escaping predators. The last years are also precarious, when the sheep are ageing and are too feeble to escape the predators.

3 At 1 year, about 7.4 years; 5 years, 5.0 years; 9 years, 2.0 years; 12 years, 0.6 years.

4 The expectancy at birth: just over seven years.

1.9 Duckweed on a pond

1 Light intensity, temperature, wind.

2 A deterioration in the weather causing drought, cold, flood, wind or reduced light intensity to affect the population. The action of herbivores.

3 Faster growth in the greenhouse.

4 Temperature.

5 Nutrient supply in the water exhausted, an inhibitor produced by the plants, space limiting.

6 The experimenter designed the series of experiments which are described in the problem.

7 **a** To see if space was the limiting factor, or if the population growth was checked by something to do with the old water (for example, lack of nutrients or presence of an inhibitor). Alternatively, the duckweed may have grown more slowly because of a physiological factor associated with its age.
b Experiment **A**.

8 Space is not a limiting factor as **C** continues to grow while the others decline. Comparing **A** and **D** with **C** and **B** suggests that the original water could somehow be a factor in the population decline. The fresh duckweed in original water **D** which does as well as **C** for four days could have been using stored nutrients.

It seems not to be entirely an ageing factor in the duckweed (compare **C** with **D**), although a comparison of **C** with **B** indicates that the original duckweed may have been in need of a tonic.

1.10 Barnacle populations

1 More eggs are produced at higher rates of flow.

2 The animals depend on an external flow of water to carry food to them. The faster the flow, the more food particles, the more growth and eventually egg production.

3 For example, ships, dock installations, piers, oil platforms, pipes carrying sea-water from the sea into industrial plant.

4 Temperature is particularly important. In cool waters fouling species take from several weeks to a year to reach maturity. Fouling is more intense in the summer. Most tropical fouling species need only about three weeks, and fouling is continuous the whole year. It is in tropical ports, therefore, that the greatest problems in the fouling of ships and industrial installations arise.

5 Competition for space: the larger the space an individual occupies, the more food it can extract from the water. Upward growth from the surface is also important because the further the animal can reach, the greater the volume of water it will be able to intercept. The features which successful sessile animals have developed are firm adhesion, occupation of as large a surface area as possible, and a high rate of growth. All these features make them troublesome on marine installations.

2

INTERACTIONS

2.1 Predator-prey relationships

1 **a** The predator population will get smaller, either by starvation or emigration.
b With the predators removed the prey population could increase.
c The prey population could be removed completely, followed rapidly by the death of the predators.
d The prey population could increase, leading perhaps to overpopulation.

2 **a** Yes. It is usually the older, weaker or sick individuals which are killed, and removal of some of the young ones keeps the breeding population down. So the prey species benefits because only the fit ones are left and there is not too much competition for food.
b Yes. Again the slower and weaker individuals do not obtain food as easily as the others, and the next generation comes from the fittest.

3 **Fig 2.1**: In this simple situation the predator was able to find and eat all the prey, and then died out itself.
  Fig 2.2: The more complex situation was more stable. The prey survived because they could escape faster than the predators could find them, and could increase elsewhere. Predator and prey thus existed together, but with periodic oscillations. At the end of the 250 days, however, the predators had died of starvation and the prey population was beginning to increase. In both, the numbers of predators are lower than those of the prey, and the predator curve closely follows that of the prey.
  In a natural ecosystem the prey would be able to escape to refuges and would not become extinct as in the first situation. It could move back into its original habitat later. There would still be fairly unstable fluctuations, but not the disappearance of one or both species.

4 **a** The lynx numbers are lower than those of the hare, and the lynx cycles follow those of the hare.
b A frequent answer here is that the hare population builds up rapidly when predator numbers are low, leading to intense intraspecific competition for food which results in a massive population decline due to starvation.
c A density dependent factor operates. MacLulich considered that an epidemic of some sort took hold and caused the deaths. He found that it was not the same disease or parasite each time, and it could vary from one part of the country to another. When the epidemic had died out due to immunity and the isolation of survivors, the hares increased from being scarce and reached a more or less constant level which could be maintained for several seasons. However, at that density the spread of some parasite or disease was inevitable. There may, of course, be other factors involved. Many other animal species have cycles of abundance.
d The time it takes the population to grow from scarcity to abundance is about the same each time round. The high density is then maintained only as long as an infection does not break out.

5 There were far too many deer for the plateau's vegetation to support. Thousands died of starvation in the next few years. The excessive grazing had seriously damaged the vegetation which did not recover to its 1906 state. The theoretical maximum carrying capacity of the plateau fell from its previous level of 30 000 deer to only 10 000. The deer population was still higher than this, and starvation was still killing more deer than predators had previously done.

6   **a** There would be a rapidly expanding pest population, which would take a great deal of time and money to control by chemicals alone, although predators could be re-imported. The new pest population may also be resistant to some insecticides. The application of the insecticide could therefore cause an increase of the pest population.

An example of such an increase comes from America. The cottony cushion scale insect (*Icerya purchasi*) accidentally introduced in 1868 from Australia increased until it seemed about to destroy the American citrus orchards where it lived. Its natural predator, a ladybird (*Novius cardinalus*), was introduced and quickly reduced the scale insect population. Later, DDT was used to try and cut down the scale insect population still further. The net result, however, was an increase in their numbers as the predator was far more susceptible to DDT than the prey. For the first time in fifty years the scale insect again became a serious problem.

b   Any other species the predator helps to control could in turn become a pest.

7   **d**

2.2   Coloration and mimicry

1   It seems that altering the colour pattern affects survival. Selection operates against colour variation.

2   **a** That the stain does not make the butterflies more attractive or more apparent, or make them look like any other prey animal; that it does not affect the animal, its life span, or its behaviour; and that it does not rapidly wear off.
b   That the treatment does not drive the butterflies away from the roost, alter behaviour in any way, or attract predators, and that the observed wing damage is due to predators and not to other causes.

3   This was a control group, showing that the stain itself had no effect as suggested in **2**.

4   The predators, having learned to avoid the unpalatable form, then keep away from the mimic.

5   In experiment 1, fewer of the conspicuous experimental moths were recaptured, indicating that they were more easily found by predators than the black control moths which blended with the background.

Experiment 2 seems confusing. Fewer experimental moths return than control ones and there seems to be no advantage in resembling a distasteful species.

Experiment 3 shows the expected result. The experimental moths seem to be at an advantage compared with the control moths. The explanation may lie in the experimental design. In experiment 2 the large number of mimics released together in the same place outnumbered the model so much that predators soon learned they were edible. In experiment 3 the mimics were spread more thinly.

The results indicate that mimicry is successful only when there are fewer mimics than models. If predators are reminded from time to time of the unpleasant experience of eating the model, they continue to refuse both model and mimic.

6   Yes.

7   More food is available to it than would otherwise be, as the poisonous food is usually avoided by other herbivores. It also provides a defence mechanism.

2.3   Interspecific competition

1   After sixteen days *Paramecium caudatum* has almost disappeared. *P. aurelia* takes longer to reach a lower stationary phase than when it is cultured alone. *P. caudatum* starts to decline after five days, after doing as well as *P. aurelia* for the first two days. As long as food was abundant and the population of each small, there was no competition. When the population became larger, competition affected both the successful and the unsuccessful species.

2   Food, space, some other nutrient.

3   Predation. Production of an inhibitor or poison. Sensitivity to bacterial waste products. In fact, *P. caudatum* is more sensitive to these waste products, giving a competitive advantage to *P. aurelia.*

4   Size. Differences in rate at which each species reproduces or dies. Ability to gain access to food, or other efficiency in food gathering. Any one of these would give a slight advantage, possibly resulting in more offspring from one species, or more deaths by starvation in the other. The successful species starts to become more numerous and eventually completely excludes the other. (See also Problem 2.7, question 2, for a similar question about plants.)

5   About twenty-five.

6   The reduced population would be spread more thinly than before over its original area and would possibly also be emigrating from it. There would therefore be more difficulty in finding mates, thus reducing the birth rate. The individuals would possibly be more exposed to predators, thus increasing the mortality.

2.4   Competitive exclusion

1   In warm moist conditions, *T. castaneum* succeeded, and in cold or dry conditions it was *T. confusum.*

2   A tolerant species can thrive in the conditions which are unsuitable for its less tolerant competitor. In this case, if both species were together in a natural habitat where there were both warm moist and cool dry conditions, *T. confusum* need not disappear although, like *T. castaneum*, it survives better in warm moist conditions. It could occupy the cold dry area and succeed there. (See also Problem 2.5, question 4, for another example.)

3   Life in the wild is more complex than inside a laboratory bottle. In other words, there could be very many factors affecting success.

4   The more heterogeneous the environment, the better. The glass tubes are a refuge for the young stages of the smaller beetle, which thus survives.

5   Density independent factors are mainly physical or **abiotic**. They include catastrophes such as storm, flood, fire, earthquake, as well as the normal variations in annual climate and daily weather. Climate may, however, sometimes act as a density dependent factor. An example given in the literature is the case of **protective refuges**. If the supply of refuges is limited, and all animals without one are killed by the weather, then this mortality would be density dependent.

Density dependent factors are mainly **biotic**. The density of a population is influenced by competition, predation, parasites and disease, all of which depend on the relative abundance of the individuals which make up that population.

Density independent factors may sometimes cause very large variations in population density. Density dependent factors tend to keep the population at, or move it towards, an average or steady-state level.

An excellent discussion of the topic is given in *Ecology* by C. J. Krebs (Harper and Row, 1972).

2.5 Specialization through competition

1   It could be physical factors which limit each species, but the evidence here seems to indicate that it is direct competition with *Balanus*. In the lower shore, disappearance of the *Chthamalus* seems to be caused in some way by the *Balanus*. This is another example of competitive exclusion seen also in Problems 2.3, 2.4 and 5.5. In fact, in the middle and lower shore, competition between the two barnacles and predation by other animals was important in determining the composition of the barnacle population. In the upper shore the physical factors of desiccation and temperature controlled the upward spread of *Balanus*.

2   Space. The heavier shelled *Balanus* grows more rapidly than *Chthamalus*. As they grow the *Balanus* shells either grow over those of the other species, or get under them, thus eventually prising them off the rock.

3   For example, allow each species to settle in the other's zone alone.

4   If the tolerance limits of the species are wide, each population can specialize at one end of the resource range. Here, both species can grow well in the lower areas of the shore, but only one can tolerate the more exposed upper reaches. (See also Problem 2.4, question 2, for another example.)

2.6 Competition and evolution

1   They will die.

2   The ones left will be those which are best able to avoid competition by utilizing a slightly different variation of the resource supply, presumably because of the normal variation between individuals. Because of the variation within the population the preferences and possibly structure, behaviour or physiology of the two species could diverge.

3   The area of overlap is considerably less, and the peaks of each population have moved some way towards the extremes.

4   In the overlapping area. This phenomenon is called **character displacement**. It seems to have occurred very many times. It provides evidence to support the theory that interspecific competition can result in ecological isolation.

5   **Fig 2.12**: There is a much greater difference in beak length between the two species where the ranges overlap but a close similarity at each end of the range where they do not meet. Beak length indicates the range of prey size taken by each species. They can occur together in the overlapping area where their beak lengths differ by exploiting different prey species.

Fig 2.13: On Daphne and Crossman islands where each species lives alone, the beak size can be taken as the optimum for each in the absence of close competitors. On the other islands, where the two occur together, the average beak size of one is shorter and of the other is longer than when alone. When together, it seems reasonable to assume that *Geospiza fortis* could survive better by eating larger seeds and *G. fuliginosa* by eating smaller, with consequent selection for slightly larger and slightly smaller beaks. Divergence of beak size thus results in co-existence and not competition.

In both cases competition could have led to divergence and the evolution of two species from a common ancestor.

2.7 Interspecific competition in plants

1 The percentage of *Agropyron* surviving in different densities of *Bromus* shows an increase as the *Bromus* becomes less dense. *Bromus* has longer roots than *Agropyron* when each is grown alone, and maintains this root growth even when in competition. The root growth of *Agropyron* suffers as there are progressively more *Bromus* plants round it.

2 Leaf area, height of plant, length of roots, high rate of growth, greater seed production, more rapid seed germination, and so on. (See also Problem 2.3, question 4 for a similar question about animals.)

In this example, *Bromus* had a 50% faster rate of root growth, and its roots grew through the winter, reaching about 90 cm below the soil surface by March. *Agropyron* roots had reached only about 14 cm by then. *Bromus* produced between 65 and 200 times more seeds than *Agropyron*, and also germinated more rapidly.

3 Light, water, carbon dioxide, oxygen, mineral salts, space for germination and establishment, possibly for pollinating or dispersing animal species.

2.8 Competition between wheat and weeds

1 a The longer the weeds are left with the wheat, the more the yield of both grain and straw drops.
b The yield of both straw and grain increases with each level of nitrogen. This is true at all levels of weeds. (Problem 4.8 gives more data on yield depressed by weeds.)

2 Yes. Straw is used for bedding and fodder for farm animals and has a number of other uses.

3 a In the presence of weeds. Between N_0 and N_8 there was about 60% increase in the number of ears per plant in the weed-infested plots (from 2.3 to 3.7). In the weed-free plots, the increase was only about 30% (4.1 to 5.3).
b Nitrogen. The greater response of the weed-infested crop to added nitrogen is evidence that nitrogen is a limiting factor.

4 a No. If it were, one would expect yields at N_8 to be similar in the plots with and without weeds.
b Water, light, other nutrients.

5 One would need to juggle figures which involved not only the hoped-for yield but also the estimated selling price of straw and grain, together with the price of fertilizer. Another consideration would be the cost of applying the fertilizer in one's own particular fields and with the labour one had available. No doubt many other factors would enter into the calculations. It could even be more profitable to grow an unfertilized, weed-infested crop than to take any action at all.

2.9 Grazing

1 They have meristems at the nodes and will therefore grow even after the top of the plant has been eaten. They may also have buds on underground stems.

2 Areas of land are enclosed, to keep out the grazers. Similar, unenclosed areas are marked out as controls. Some species will become more common as others disappear. The area will eventually be invaded by larger species.

3 The effects of grazing depend on the competitive ability of the species which make up the pasture. Some will be poor competitors and do better when others are constantly being removed by grazing. Good competitors, however, may not do so well with grazing. Many grow best in medium vegetation with some, but not much, grazing. When grazing stops, shrubs and finally trees take over a pasture, with a possible reduction in the number of species.

The effects of grazing, then, on the number of species depends on the amount and type of grazing, its timing, and whether it is continuous or intermittent.

2.10 Intraspecific competition in plants

1 In Fig 2.14 the lower line shows a very early stage which was non-competitive. The yield is directly proportional to the number of plants per unit area. As the plants grow larger, the yield per unit area stops increasing so directly with the density. At 181 days the maximum yield is reached at a low density and not increased.

2 The plants were presumably competing for light. As they grew larger and shaded each other the yield per unit area rapidly reached a maximum which could not be increased with more plants there. (See also Problems 4.2, 4.3 for further points on yield and leaves.)

3 Shepherd's purse was planted at densities of 1, 5, 50, 100 and 200 seeds per pot. The number of seeds produced by each plant was counted. The total number of seeds produced per pot remains very approximately the same, but the number per plant obviously decreases enormously, because of competition for the limited resources.

4 Too dense a crop means wasting seed, even if the harvest yield is the same as for a sparse crop, and may mean the need for more fertilizer and other things than would be necessary for a less dense crop. It would also be easier for disease or pest to spread rapidly.

On the other hand, a fairly dense crop makes maximum use of the available light. It does not waste land, or allow too many weeds, and may be easier to spray and harvest. Problem 4.2 discusses density in relation to yield.

5 Yes. They then make the best use of the available resources, and there will be some which survive if the conditions change somewhat.

Intraspecific competition of a more subtle nature in an animal species could be illustrated by reference to Problem 1.6 which refers to hamsters in a confined environment. There is abundant food and absence of predators, but not enough space for the population to expand. The number of live offspring produced is very low and the effects of density seem to be felt through interference with breeding and maternal physiology and behaviour.

2.11   Inhibition

1   Competition for food, for space or some other resource, the effect of waste products. (See also Problem 1.9 for inhibition or competition by *Lemna*.)

2   For example, take culture water in which large tadpoles have been growing and put small tadpoles in it on their own.

3   a The plants are in separate test tubes in experiment D.
b   There is a plastic partition in the soil in experiment C.

4   Experiment A.

5   To see if there was intraspecific competition.

6   The inhibitor must come from the leaves or other above-ground part. When water was added to the soil from the side there was no reduction in yield. When it was added from above there was.

2.12   Flies and bacteria

1   A variety of media could be used to isolate and culture micro-organisms obtained from a fly, and the micro-organisms then identified.

2   Flies visiting the source of infection could be sprayed with a dye and recaptured later. In some experiments a fluorescein dye, which shows up only under ultra-violet light, was used.

3   The fly could be exposed to a number of different types of media to obtain and culture as many as possible of the micro-organisms, and the colonies then counted.

4   Add a dried concentrate of the bacteria to the bacteria-free medium.

5   It could be a symbiotic co-operative relationship. There is certainly benefit to the larvae, but nothing is said about the bacteria. It seems not to be a case of para-sitism. It could be predation, although the larvae could be benefiting not from the bacteria themselves but from a substance found in or excreted by the bacteria.
    It was shown that the larvae developed normally when supplied with a dried concentrate of the bacterium *Escherichia coli*.

3

ECOLOGICAL ENERGETICS

3.1 Energy entering communities

1 About 30% to 40% is reflected back into space by clouds or dust. Another 10% to 20% is converted to heat energy by absorption by gases, water vapour or dust. Only something like 50% to 60% reaches the earth's surface, even on a clear day at noon. Even then, about 40% is reflected back into space by the earth's surface, and some is absorbed by water, bare earth or vegetation.

2 The amount reaching the outer atmosphere depends on latitude. The amount reaching the ground depends on the season, the time of day and the amount of cloud.

3 Most of the light absorbed by plants is converted directly to heat and lost by re-radiation or transpiration.

4 Energy can be lost as heat and in respiration from all organisms. Some is transferred from plants and incorporated into the tissues of decomposers or herbivores, and later carnivores. It may be egested, excreted or used in reproduction. Some is exported as animals move or plants are taken away and is lost to the community which produced it. Some is tied up in dead organic matter and is lost to the community for a time, sometimes millions of years in the case of oil, coal or peat, before it yields up its energy. (See also Problem 3.7, and 3.8 question 6 which make a similar point.)

3.2 Primary productivity

1 **a** Carbon dioxide, light intensity, duration of light (day length), temperature.
b Water, temperature, nutrients, space.

2 Irrigate and fertilize the land where water and nutrients are limiting productivity. Remove weeds and pests. Both productivity and yield have been raised in some new varieties of plants produced by plant-breeders.

Man can also affect primary productivity by reducing it, something which has occurred many times by over-exploitation of land and a non-understanding of **biogeochemical cycles**: the circulation of matter from the environment to living organisms and back again.

(See also Problem 4.1, and 4.3 question 2.)

3 With more mouths to feed it becomes very important to see exactly which factor or factors are limiting the yield of a crop so that the limit can be removed or extended and yield increased. Some of the new 'wonder' wheat and rice varieties have been bred with upright leaves, which increase the leaf area index (see Problem 4.2) without extra shading of the lower leaves. In addition, a full understanding of the factors which affect the productivity of natural ecosystems would enable us to protect them and prevent pollution of them and of our water.

4 Those where light, temperature and water are favourable for photosynthesis all the year, and where lack of nutrients does not limit growth. Tropical rain forests and tropical coral reefs are examples. Hot areas of the world, however, contain a lot of unproductive dry areas such as desert and dry grassland, as well as deep lakes and oceans. In arctic areas the daily rate of production can be quite high in the short growing season when days are long, but the annual rate is low. (See also Problem 3.4.)

5 Net production is the formation of new plant tissue. Gross production is net production plus respiration.

6 The net production may become part of the plant for its lifetime, or become seeds, fruits or perennating organs. It may be consumed by herbivores or parasites or, on death, by decomposers. It may be converted to cotton or flax, hemp or sisal, tobacco, coal, peat or oil and in some form or other be used by people.

7 The older, larger, trees have a higher proportion of non-photosynthesising but respiring tissue such as roots and phloem. There will be more shading of lower leaves in older than in younger trees.

8 See Fig 3.11.

Fig 3.11 Gross and net production for a typical annual plant

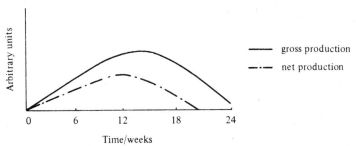

9 It is useful to know when to harvest in order to get the maximum yield for the minimum effort. It is often uneconomic to cultivate plants much beyond the time of maximum net production. It is also useful to know which parts of a plant supply the material for the edible storage organs (see Problem 4.6).

3.3 Leaves and productivity

1 Leaves often grow to give a mosaic (Fig 3.3), giving maximum leaf exposure to the light and minimum shading of lower leaves. Leaves at right angles to the direction of the light will intercept more than those growing closer to the stem. A plant shaped like a wide-based cone, with its axis pointing to the sun, and leaves set spirally down the stem, gives a good arrangement. (See also Problem 4.2 for a comment on leaf angle and yield in relation to crop density.)

2 3, 2, 4, 1.

3 Up to maximum productivity, the more leaves the better. With too many leaves there will be shading of lower ones by those above. The shaded ones may even use more in respiration than they produce in photosynthesis and thus be a drain on the plant.

4 Young, actively growing leaves will have a high rate of respiration and a high rate of production of new tissue. Old leaves will respire, but probably have a low

16

rate of photosynthesis. The more young and mature leaves and the fewer old ones the better.

5 Light interception is affected by leaf thickness and the number of layers of cells with chloroplasts. Leaves in sunny places, when compared with leaves of plants of the same species growing in a shaded place, usually have a smaller surface area, are thicker, and have chloroplast-containing cells extending further down through the leaf. Shade leaves are thin and large. Their chloroplasts may move inside the cells to lie parallel with the leaf surface. Some plants have leaves which can change their angle with the stem. They then lie edge-on to strong sunlight which could damage the cells.

3.4 Productivity round the world

Problems 3.4 and 3.5 look at the same data in two slightly different ways. They both aim to contrast primary productivity in natural ecosystems and consider some reasons for the differences. See also Problem 4.1 for crop production contrasted with that of natural ecosystems.

1 Water, nutrients, length of the growing season.

2 a Nutrients, light penetration.
b Water.
c Length of the growing season, temperature.

3 The differences between different groups of plants could be brought out: algae in the deep ocean and angiosperms in the desert are quite different, but have similar productivities, as also are algae in coral reefs and sugar cane. The relative theoretical productivities of grass compared with trees, or evergreen forests compared with deciduous forests, could be discussed.

3.5 Productivity and ecosystems

1 The tropical forest, which has a high gross productivity because it assimilates all the year round, also loses more than the temperate forest by respiration because of the high average temperatures throughout the year. The temperate forest loses its leaves for half the year, when the low temperatures and dormant state of the plants mean that little energy is used in respiration.

2 a Tropical forests and crops, swamplands. Water supply, favourable temperature, long growing season.
b Those where production is limited by water, low temperatures, or length of the growing season and light intensity.

3 The plant roots are in water, and the above-ground parts are in full light and air. There is quick bacterial decomposition in the soil, releasing plenty of nutrients for plant growth.

4 Roots, fallen leaves and leaves eaten by herbivores are not included, neither are the products used in respiration. For perennials the method uses material more than one year old.

5 By the production of oxygen: not a very useful method for communities growing on land, although sometimes used for aquatic communities. By the uptake of carbon dioxide or the disappearance of mineral nutrients. By the use of radioactive materials.

3.6 Nutrients and thermoclines: productivity in the sea

1 Algae and higher plants growing on mudbanks and in salt-marshes contribute to the high productivity of estuaries. There are plenty of nutrients because of the mixing of water layers, which does not often happen in the open sea. Nutrients are also carried down by the river. On the other hand, light penetration may be lower than in the open sea because of the silt and other material brought down by the river.

2 **a** Light (both the duration and the intensity increase), temperature, nutrients.
b Grazing by zooplankton and the loss of nutrients through the thermocline.
c The replenishment of nutrients in the surface water layer due to the breakdown of the thermocline, the temperature of the water is still relatively high and the zooplankton population is low due to starvation.

3 In tropical seas there is a permanent thermocline which results in severe nutrient depletion in the epilimnion. In an upwelling area, or a coral reef, primary productivity is high. An upwelling area results also in increased secondary productivity. Some important fisheries, for example off the coasts of Peru and south California, are in such areas. A figure for Peru is given in Table 4.7.

4 A thermocline does not develop as the surface water never warms up enough. There is therefore mixing of the water, and lack of nutrients is not a limiting factor in plant growth. The limiting factors here are the duration and intensity of light, and temperature (see also Problems 3.4 and 3.5 for discussion of external factors and productivity).

3.7 Ecological efficiency

1 As heat, in respiration, as exported material.

2 About ten per cent.

3 More than half goes to decomposers rather than to the herbivores. This is a point which becomes very important when one considers the recycling of materials (see Problem 3.9) or pasture on which grazing farm animals feed.

4 Import here means animals or overhanging vegetation which drop into the pond, or detritus brought into it by water run-off or by streams.
Export means material carried away in a flow of water or by animals, or movement from the system of mobile animals.

3.8 Consumers and food chains

1 Broadly, **consumers** eat animals or plants, or parts of them, or substances such as cell sap, blood or nectar, produced by them. Their food is living or produced by living organisms, or sometimes recently dead, or recently egested matter. All animals are consumers.
Decomposers get their food from dead animals or plants, or parts of them, or excreted or egested matter. Fungi and bacteria are decomposers, also some other saprophytic or semi-saprophytic plants, actinomycetes, slime moulds and some protistans. Many small invertebrates help decomposition by breaking up the material as they feed on it.
There are some exceptions. The plant dodder is a heterotroph, some fungi are parasitic, and some plants catch and digest insects. In addition some species are intermediate and others can change their mode of nutrition.

2   Herbivores eat plants.

Carnivores eat other animals.

Omnivores eat animals and plants.

Detritivores feed on the dead remains of animals and plants, on litter or detritus which is organic debris such as the accumulated material under trees or on the bottom of a pond consisting of whole or parts of dead organisms.

Scavengers feed mainly on dead animals or the dung of animals. They include blowfly larvae, crabs, and larger animals such as crows, vultures and hyenas.

Parasites live in or on a living organism and get their food from it.

3   This exercise makes the point, picked up in the paragraph after question **4**, that the situation is not clear cut.

6   It is used in respiration and the maintenance of body temperature in birds and mammals. It leaves the animal in faeces or excretory material, as gametes or new individuals, and a large portion goes to the decomposers. (See also Problem 3.1, question 4, and Problem 3.7 for discussion of a similar point.)

3.9   Decomposers

Problem 3.8 also mentions decomposers.

1   Decomposers enable material to be recycled. They release nutrients which would otherwise be locked up in dead organisms. They increase the fertility of the soil which is thus able to support more producers.

2   Earthworms and larger invertebrates. Without them breakdown is much slower.

3   **a** Breakdown is faster in autumn and early winter.

b   Temperature, water and oxygen will affect the activity of the invertebrates and micro-organisms. A waterlogged soil can be nearly anaerobic. A soil solution with a low pH will exclude many organisms.

4   Bacteria and fungi had used leaf material in their metabolism, but without making holes in the leaf.

5   There would be leaching by water causing loss of materials from the leaf, and a breakdown of chlorophyll causing colour changes. They would also gain water and become sodden. Dry leaves on the surface of the soil were not broken down as quickly as the buried, wet, leaves.

6   In communities where invertebrate and micro-organism activity is low for one reason or another. Fens and bogs have too extreme a pH, arctic communities produce little litter but it accumulates because of low temperatures and a waterlogged soil. In other communities the air is too dry and the temperature too high in summer, or too low in winter, for decomposers to survive or be active all the year round.

3.10   Pyramids

1   For example: tree, herbivorous insects, birds (see question **4**).

2   Not if all sources of food energy in the community are considered, as energy is lost in the transfer from one stage to the next. A pyramid of energy is always the right way up, a natural effect of the second law of thermodynamics.

3   The **pyramid of numbers** can vary widely in different communities, depending on whether the producers are small or large. In addition, numbers at different levels can be so different that it is not easy to show the whole community on the same scale. The data might then be better presented in some other way. A number pyramid might, however, be the most useful to consider in a study made by sixth formers.

The **pyramid of biomass** is more useful, except when the producers are very much smaller than the consumers. In that case, the mass of the consumers could occasionally be greater than that of the producers, but the quick turnover of producers gives a large output from a small standing crop. Phytoplankton and zooplankton (**4d**) can give this sort of situation at certain times of the year. Fig 3.6 in Problem 3.6 shows a typical phytoplankton curve. The zooplankton curve would follow that for the phytoplankton, and would occasionally be higher than it.

The **energy pyramid** introduces a time factor. The other two pyramids show a picture of the standing state, whereas this one represents organisms produced per unit time (say, one year). It therefore gives the best overall view of the community.

4   a 3,   b 5,   c 1,   d 4,   e 2.

3.11   Man as a consumer

1   Plants. If ecological efficiency (see Problem 3.7) is about ten per cent, then only one-tenth of the plant material consumed by herbivores is passed on to the second level consumer, and one-tenth of that to the third level. If, however, we remain omnivorous, then a mixture of plant and first level consumers is the most economical.

2   Most of our domestic food animals are herbivores.

3   Plants do not contain all the essential amino acids and are low in some vitamins. Compared with meat they are high in carbohydrates, but relatively low in proteins. They are immovable, and therefore easily spoiled by inclement weather at the wrong time. Custom, preference and taste should also be considered.

We now know, however, that we do not need the large amounts of animal protein recommended only a few years ago. Grain, potatoes and legumes can supply protein needs. Gastronomically, dishes based on such staple foods could be enlivened by small amounts of meat and by spices and vegetables.

4   Basically, use more of the earth's surface for plant growth. For example, irrigate and fertilize the deserts, add warmth and light to colder climes. Solar heating would save conventional fuels for something more useful than burning.

5   If one ignores the economics of looking after 300 rabbits (instead of a single bullock) even for only 30 days and killing and skinning them, then the answer would be rabbits. They produce the same amount of food as the bullock, but in one-quarter of the time.

6   At the end of the fastest growing period. To keep them longer is wasteful.

7   Reduce the amount of plant material eaten by non-food animals and decomposers. One example would be to harvest and process the plants and bring the product to the herbivore, rather than letting cows share the grass with other herbivores. Only about one-seventh of the primary production of a grassland goes to the cattle on it. Other herbivores and decomposers take the remainder. Theoretically, therefore, the yield of the cattle could be seven times as great.

Reduce respiratory losses in animals by not allowing them free movement. Closely tethered veal calves, or the way in which chickens are produced, could be considered as examples. Loss of freedom for domestic animals can be balanced against more and cheaper food. Chickens are now within the reach of most at 70 to 80 pence a kg. Before their mass production they were luxury items.

8 For discussion. Fish flour, plankton, plant protein, bacteria grown on oil wastes, soya beans, unusual types of shellfish, zebra, antelope, manatees and capybaras (see Problem 1.3 question 5), even sheep's eyes, ants, locusts and Welsh 'lava-bread' could extend their range as acceptable foods.

4

CROP PRODUCTION

4.1 Crop productivity

The most important applications of photosynthesis, productivity and limiting factors are in food production. The problems in this chapter form a useful extension to those in chapter 3.

1   The conditions which gave the figures in columns 3 and 6 were much more favourable for photosynthesis. Most crops have a high rate of production for some months, and then none for the rest of the year. Some crops such as sugar cane, algae and rice to a lesser extent, have production continuing throughout the year.

2   For discussion. Major limiting factors such as the main climatic divisions can hardly be removed. Water and nutrients can be added, at a cost. (See also Problem 3.2.)

3   The more productive of the natural ecosystems have daily figures which compare favourably with figures in columns 2 and 5 for the daily productivity of crops.

4.2 Leaves and yield

1   Light falls onto bare ground and is lost to the plants. In addition, there is more space for weeds.

2   There could be depredation by disease and pests which can spread more rapidly in a dense monoculture. On the other hand, the crop will be easier to irrigate, spray and harvest and may save in labour and material what is lost by a decreased yield. Problem 2.10, question 4 discusses density with regard to competition.

3   $\frac{4}{1} = 4$

4   Probably not, as there would be more shading of the lower leaves. A variety of other factors may also be involved.

5   The angle between leaf and stem allows greater light interception and less shading of lower leaves. (See also Problem 3.3.) Also, about 90% of the yield of some species of grain-bearing plants is due to photosynthesis in the flag leaf and ear (see Problem 4.6). Hence any shading of lower leaves will have relatively little effect on yield.

6   A large amount of fossil energy is used to make and operate machines, to make fertilizers, pesticides and herbicides, to power irrigation or drainage schemes, and so on.

4.3 Leaves and the growing season

1   At least as far as a LAI of 3, the productivity increases with an increase of leaf surface per unit of ground.

2   The aerial environment can hardly be altered in open fields at the present, although the future may see some form of glasshouse, or other, extension to arable land. Artificial light sources, however, are likely to be even more costly than now.

New varieties of crop which produce leaves rapidly would bring forward the period of maximum production. A field with more than one species of crop plant, each having maximum growth at different times, might help to extend the growing period at both ends, although there would be other problems of ease of farming. Frost-resistant varieties (e.g. of potatoes) would give a higher LAI while the days are long. Leaf area in spring might possibly be increased by auxin sprays. Perennial evergreen crops such as pasture or coniferous forest overcome some of the disadvantages of annual crops but are hardly interchangeable with them.

In glasshouse culture, of course, it is possible to increase and prolong illumination, raise the temperature and even add carbon dioxide, enabling plants to grow well outside the growing season, but at a large energy cost.

4.4   Factors affecting leaf area index and unit leaf rate

1   Fertilizer: LAI. Produces more and larger leaves.
Water: LAI. In drought conditions both LAI and ULR decrease.
Light intensity: ULR. High light intensity will reduce leaf area by reducing leaf expansion.
Light duration: ULR.
Temperature: LAI. Accelerates the production and expansion of leaves.
Carbon dioxide: ULR.
Improvement in crop husbandry: LAI. For example, methods of sowing or planting which give a more uniformly spaced crop at a reasonable density will give a uniformly high LAI. Rotation of crops and inclusion of legumes can increase the supply of nitrogen for later crops and therefore affect both LAI and ULR.

2   Probably the size. The leafiness, and especially the duration of the leafiness, is important (see Problem 4.3), but yield can only be increased by increased size up to a certain point as more and more leaves are shaded.

3   Biological yield is the total net production of the plant. Economic yield is that which can be harvested and used by people.

4   Genetics and plant breeding. The plant's genes determine how much of the net production is located in a part of the plant we can harvest and use as food or other useful material (grain, edible leaves, sugar, fruit, fibre, wood).

4.5   Factors affecting plant productivity

a   b   c   d   f   g   k   l   m   n

This problem includes many of the teaching points made in Problems 4.1 to 4.4, and in some chapter 3 problems.

4.6   What makes a barley grain?

1   For example, keep the leaves of experimental plants in darkness and the ear in light. Compare grain mass with that of control plants.

2   The flag leaf has contributed to the growth of the grains, but equally to each.

It cannot account for the differences between grains at the base and tip of the ear.

3   The awn lengths correlate closely with the growth rate of each grain.

4   The results support the hypothesis that each awn contributes mainly to its own grain. (However, the figures are percentages, not the mass of materials produced. We do not know from these figures if the awn contributes all the material which makes the differences between grains.)

5   The sources are the flag leaf and the awns. The sink is the grain.

6   There could be plant-breeding programmes for varieties with large or long-living sources. In this case the size and length of life of the awns could be the things to breed for.

4.7   Photosynthesis during one day

1   The number of leaf discs used should be high, and the same throughout. 100 discs, each one centimetre in diameter, would be suitable at each time of sampling. They should all be taken from leaves of about the same age, which are actively photosynthesizing, and in similar positions on the plant. The leaves should be dried for about five hours before weighing.

2   Plotting column 2, the cumulative increase, shows only a steady increase and a drop after 20.00 hours. A graph constructed using the changes in dry mass, when each measurement is deducted from the following one, shows the day's fluctuations.

3   5 am to noon shows an increase, due to an increasing rate of photosynthesis associated with increasing light intensity.
    Noon to 14.00 hours shows a drop which could be due to one or more factors. The light intensity could be inhibitory, carbon dioxide limiting as all plants are photosynthesizing at their maximum, or respiration high because of the high temperature. Assimilates are perhaps being translocated away from the leaves, temporary shade or overcast sky may be reducing light intensity, or wilting could be leading to stomatal closure and thus prevention of gas exchange.
    At 14.00 hours there seems to be a reversal of the previous factor(s), leading to an increased rate. Between 16.00 and 22.00 hours the rate of photosynthesis decreases as the light intensity becomes lower. After 20.00 hours respiratory losses exceed photosynthetic gains and the compensation point is passed. In addition, translocation will cause the leaves to lose mass.

4.8   Weeds

1   By competition for soil nutrients or water, or by shading, weeds can retard the growth of crop plants. They can make harvesting difficult, and also reduce the value of the harvest if weed seeds are included. They can cause people, machines, chemicals, and hence time and cash, to be tied up in weed removal. Some weeds in pastures may be poisonous to grazing farm animals, or fruits and seeds may become embedded in the fleece of sheep. (Problem 2.8 gives data on wheat and weeds.)

2   Improving the soil in any way for the desired plants also makes conditions more suitable for weeds. Harvesting by machine can aid dispersal of weed seeds. Seeds or reproductive vegetative parts such as potato tubers left in the ground from one crop can become weeds in the next one. In pastures, overgrazing which creates bare patches, or undergrazing allowing weeds to become established, can encourage weed appearance and seed production.

3 Cultivation, either ploughing or hoeing by hand or machine, removes weeds, but it involves a lot of labour and is costly. It can also bring dormant weed seeds to the surface where they germinate, or cut up and disperse vegetative reproductive organs such as rhizomes. Spraying with a weedkiller is another method. So is growing crop plants at higher densities, as the more bare ground the more weeds. Using 'clean' seed, free from weed seeds, for sowing crops removes one source of weeds.

4 The yield of both crops is greater without weeds .

For beet, weeds between the rows have a greater competitive effect on the growth of beet than the weeds in the rows.

For carrots, weeds germinating at the same time as the crop give the crop a very poor start. The closer the spacing of the crop, the more difficult it is for the weeds to become established.

5 For discussion. Problem 4.10 also discusses costs involved in growing a crop, in this case cucumbers.

4.9   Potato blight

1 Wet, warm weather. When the temperature has been above 12.8 °C and the relative humidity higher than 75% for more than 24 hours, warnings are given to potato farmers through the medium of radio, television and the press.

2 The longer the fungus is present, the more damage it can do and the greater the loss of production. Translocation to the tubers will be reduced and tuber growth limited. By September the tubers are ready for harvesting, so a late attack will affect fewer tubers.

3 In March, April and May the temperature is unlikely to be optimal for fungal growth.

4 By clearing all unwanted tubers and burning diseased plant material. By growing resistant strains or early varieties, and by using certified, disease-free seed potatoes, or checking seed potatoes are free from blight before planting.

4.10   Cucumbers and costs

1 The crop sells for more cash.

2 If only one condition is to be increased, choose light intensity if the return is worth the investment. Light intensity then boosts yield from 14 kg to 25 kg. If two conditions, choose light intensity and carbon dioxide which together increase yield to 59 kg.

3 Increasing light intensity and carbon dioxide costs £3x and other costs bring the total to £4x. The sale of 59 kg cucumbers yields £5.9x. This is a profit of 47.5%, before tax.

Increasing all three adds another £3x for heating, bringing the total outlay to £7x. The sale gives £7.9x, a profit of 12.8% before tax.

4 Yes. Costs are £7x, possibly less because of the few weeks when they would not be needed. Sales are now £15.8x, a profit of 126%.

5 For example:
Light: fluorescent lighting.
Heat: central heating pipes.

Carbon dioxide: a heater which burns propane, natural gas or paraffin also produces carbon dioxide; dry carbon dioxide. Adding large amounts of manure adds carbon dioxide by the respiration of micro-organisms. (Recently it has been discovered that nitrogen oxide (nitric oxide) produced by paraffin and propane burners interferes with photosynthesis and can retard growth of tomato plants by 30%.)

Problem 4.8 also discusses costs, in this case in relation to weeding a crop.

4.11 Fish productivity

1 **ab** Fish are not primary producers, as are the plants in Table 4.1. Herbivores would finally yield only about 10% of the food they eat. Some of the data is for carnivorous fish which would give only a 10% yield of the first level consumers they eat.

The products of photosynthesis by algae in the sea are eaten by many species of fish and other animals, only a few of which are harvested by us.

c The more primary production there is in an area, the more fish that area can support.

2 For discussion. For example, fishponds have long been used to produce fish; as long ago as 1100 BC there were fishponds in China, where carp were reared. Fish farming now accounts for about 4% of the world's edible fish production. Experiments have also been done on adding fertilizer to inland waters to give more food in the food chain by raising primary productivity. Some fish are reared in hatcheries and then released into the sea. Even the warm water effluent from power stations can be used for fish rearing to give an increased growth rate.

5

COMMUNITY ECOLOGY

5.1 Factors affecting ecosystems

There is an enormous number of ecosystems, and in many cases the boundary between one ecosystem and another is not clearly defined. However, it is possible to classify ecosystems which contain communities of similar organisms, and also to see where they occur either across the British Isles or over the whole world.

Most communities are classified according to the dominant vegetation, but similar assemblages of animal species are to be found within similar ecosystems. Usually, similar ecosystems are found in similar environmental conditions. In widely separated parts of the world, however, areas with a similar environment may support communities with similar structure, but a different species composition.

The distribution of communities is controlled in the end by the physical factors of the environment, especially by the climate. A geographical distribution of ecosystems can enable one to identify the physical or biotic factors which influence the development and maintenance of particular sorts of community.

This problem asks students to try to work out the broad principles of geographical distribution and ecological factors. Without guidance or interpolated teaching, however, they may go off at a tangent or find it vague. It therefore best suits a discussion approach rather than a purely written answer.

Good surveys of the major points are to be found in *Ecology* by R. E. Ricklefs (Nelson, 2nd Ed. 1980); *Natural Ecosystems* by W. B. Clapham (Collier-Macmillan, 1973); *Ecology* by E. P. Odum (Holt, Rinehart and Winston, 1975).

5.2 Succession and climax

1   Probably yes.

2   Yes, unless some external factor prevents a long succession from continuing. Storms, fire, disease or climatic cycles make long-term successions less predictable than short-term ones.

3   Small annual plants, larger ones, perennial herbs, shrubs, small trees.

4   Gradually.

5   The effect which the community has on the habitat will change the habitat and make it less favourable for the species already there. A simple example is seen in a species which grows well in the thin dry soil of a patch of exposed bare ground. Its growth there causes the accumulation of humus as well as damp and shady conditions underneath it. Species less tolerant of the initial conditions, and better able to compete than the first species in the second stage, become established in its place.

In addition, species which invade the community will also change the environment.

6 When species new to the community no longer change the environment within the community. For example, shrubs invading grassland, or trees following the shrubs would both drastically affect the existing vegetation and thus the constitution of the whole community. However, once climax woodland or forest has become established, then so have the major environmental factors within the forest.

7 The climate, latitude, height above sea level, edaphic factors to do with the soil, biotic factors (see also Problem 5.1).

5.3   The number of species in a community

1   a The available resources can be exploited much more efficiently by many species with differing requirements than by few.

b A higher number of species adds variety to the physical environment, and gives many more places for other species to live. It creates more microhabitats and provides different food.

c With more species there will be more interspecific competition, perhaps leading to change and evolution which would not be possible with only one or a few species.

2 The relation between number of species and latitude must be due to some climatic factor or factors: temperature, rainfall, seasonality, daylength, light intensity and so on.

3 For discussion. For reference, *Ecology* by R. E. Ricklefs (Nelson, 2nd Ed: 1980) and *Ecology* by C. J. Krebs (Harper and Row, 2nd Ed: 1978) give a good discussion on the number of species in a community.

5.4   Rocky shores

1 Graph.

2 The major zones are between 0 and 3 metres, 3 and 11 metres, 11 and 16 metres.

3 Low water exposes the organisms to desiccation, fresh water as rain, temperature extremes, higher light intensities, predation by land and aerial predators. There will also be problems connected with food and nutrient supply, gas exchange and support when exposed by the tides. Other factors are wave action and the size of the rock for attachment.

4 There are many adaptations. The plants may have thick cell walls and be mucilaginous, or possess some other feature which helps to prevent water loss. Air vesicles and intercalary meristems may be present, plus a holdfast and a flexible but resistant thallus.
Many of the animals possess a hard shell with the ability to close apertures in it, and maybe some means of adhering to the rock.

5.5   Calcicole and calcifuge

1   a One experimental design is given in the problem. To compare growth when in a normal situation with many other competing species, plants could be sown in or transplanted to different areas where there was undisturbed vegetation. Performance there could be compared with growth on nearby cleared areas of bare ground. Replicates would be needed, and a means of measuring growth.

b Number germinated, or subsequent length of life, height at various times, final fresh and dry mass, and so on.

2 Students might expect that only the calcicole would grow on chalk soil and the calcifuge on acid soil.

3 Interspecific competition when the two are grown together, and competitive exclusion.

The fact that both species will grow on both types of soil again (see Problems 2.3, 2.4, 2.5) demonstrates that the wider the limits of tolerance of a species, the better chance it has of survival when competing. Each species is better adapted than the other to one of the two habitats.

5.6 Earthworms in the soil

1 Graph.

2 Hot and cold weather correlate with fewer worms in the top 15 cm of soil. Worms are numerous only in fairly warm wet weather.

3 The earthworm population was lower prior to May, but had been increasing before November. Leaf fall occurs in the autumn.

4 Perhaps 15 cm was not deep enough, all humus-containing soil should have been included. The mean monthly rainfall figure could be misleading. A better figure might have been that for rainfall in the few days before sampling. Soil temperature might have been more useful than air temperature. More than one sample should have been taken each month.

5.7 Sampling

1 Two graphs.

2 The second, where the points fall almost on a straight line showing that the probability of capture remains constant. Total population would be about 160.

3 $\frac{75 \times 60}{48} = 94$

4 That the marked animals mix freely and at random with the unmarked ones. That they are neither more easy nor more difficult to catch the next time. (Some animals become 'trap-happy' and return again and again for the bait in the trap.) That there are no births, deaths or movements from or into the population.

5 a A,   b C,   c B,   d A,   e A,   f C.

5.8 Rat population sampling

1 $\frac{55 \times 24}{20} = 66$

2 **a** Try the old traps in the place where most rats were caught, and see if they catch the expected number or fewer.

b Try the new traps in the new place again, and see if a lower proportion than expected of marked rats is caught.

c   Repeat the trapping in the second area, and see if there is a similar drop in the number caught.

d   Continue trapping and estimating population size.

5.9   The Aswan High Dam

1   A regular supply of irrigation water, making the lean parts of the year far more productive and raising the standard of living of those who survive on farming. A constant supply of electricity generated at the dam, and the money earned by exporting some of it. A by-product is the increased yield of edible fish upstream of the dam, up to about 100 times more than before.

2   Possibly not. As more food becomes available and the standard of living rises, more people survive. There may come a time when the population is so much larger that it is back where it was. The dam was officially declared finished and ready on January 15th 1971. Between September 1972 and December 1973 the population of Egypt increased from 35 to 36 million. In 1976 it was 38 million, growing at an annual rate of 2.2 per cent.

3   Those given in the text:
Loss of fertile silt downstream of the dam, which means that more money than before must be spent on fertilizers.
Drastic reduction in the sardine catch.
The Nile is not scoured downstream of the dam as well as it was before. The delta coastline, without the annual outpouring of flood water, is more open to erosion by sea currents. There is also a rise in soil salinity near the delta, with consequent effect on crop growing there.
A serious effect is the increase in those parasites which are more successful when there are large areas of still water. This must greatly affect the lives of many more people, and increase the amount of money which should be spent on control or eradication of the parasites and treatment of sufferers.
The loss of many irreplaceable ancient artefacts.
In addition, the relatively still water of Lake Nasser encourages the growth of plants. One is the water hyacinth which may clog up the water, or alternatively be useful in providing food for domesticated animals.
One serious problem is the waterlogging of farmland where the subsoil water cannot now drain quickly enough to the underlying gravels. A 30-year programme of drainage works has begun. Without drainage about a third of the area may become unproductive within 35 years, and crop yields may be reduced elsewhere.

5.10   Life on Mars?

1   Photosynthesis.

2   Soil which was not exposed to $^{14}CO_2$ was also illuminated and otherwise treated in the same way. Soil was heated to a temperature which would kill any organisms, and then treated in the same way as the experimental soil.

3   Respiration.

6

POLLUTION

6.1 Freshwater pollution

1   **a** 1 oxygen
    2 BOD
    3 suspended solids

b   The level of dissolved oxygen is high in unpolluted water, and then rapidly falls as it is used by the decomposers. At this time the BOD is high. Suspended solids drop to normal as the added material sinks or disappears.

2   **a** 1 oxygen
    2 BOD
    The hot water further lowers the level of dissolved oxygen and raises the BOD.

b   There is less oxygen in clean fresh water at higher summer temperatures.

3   *Cladophora* and the other algae grow well in the higher levels of nitrate and phosphate ions. The luxuriant growth of the algae is called an **algal bloom.**

4   Oxygen.

5   Tubifex.

6   Clean streams flowing into it and diluting the polluted water. Turbulent water hastens re-oxygenation and carries suspended solids for longer. Heavy rain.

7   Usually, standard physical and chemical tests are adequate to determine pollution in prevention work. But in many cases, complementary biological methods have proved to be of value in giving a better picture of the conditions. Indicator organisms show when pollution reaches critical levels.

8   Excessive pollution of the lake will cause the same reduction in dissolved oxygen, and result in similar algal blooms. The process is called **eutrophication.** The water becomes unpleasant for leisure activities, and even unhealthy for swimmers. Fish die, as well as other organisms. The dead animals clog up water-works, smell, and look unsightly. If pollution is stopped, it can take many years before the eco-system is back to normal, relying on the natural flow of water. In the Great Lakes in North America, the estimate is about twenty years for 90% of the waste to be cleared from Lake Erie (which has about 4800 km of highly industrialized shore line) and Lake Ontario, and hundreds of years for Lakes Superior and Michigan.

6.2 Air pollution

1   Across the city centre there is a lichen desert. Thereafter the number of species of lichen slowly increases. The lichen flora increases first on asbestos, then on sandstone and then on tree-trunks, suggesting that the type of substrate affects the ability of lichens to survive.

2   The tree lichen desert lasts longest.

3   There is no vertical rise of warm air, and pollutants are trapped in the cool belt. Normally the rising warm surface air carries the pollutants with it. In inversion the cool surface air is trapped under the warm air, making a lid over the city and concentrating pollutants. Only when the weather changes does the inversion stop. In Los Angeles thermal inversions occur about a hundred days each year.

4   For discussion.

6.3   Bronchitis

Fig 6.9 shows that cough and phlegm are more frequent in heavy smokers than in non-smokers, and heavier than in ex-smokers. Bronchitic illness is absent from non-smokers. We do not know where these men lived, so cannot relate Fig 6.9 with normal air pollution. Fig 6.8 shows that bronchitics are almost as good indicators of pollution as are lichens.

The limits of 250/500 for smoke and sulphur dioxide have since become the unofficial target for the clean air campaign in the UK. In the 1952 London smog levels of 400/2000 were reached. By the mid-1970s only about 30 of the 1250 sites surveyed in the UK were over the 250/500 limits for 24 hours.

6.4   Copper tolerance

1   One would expect any plants or seeds taken from a normal environment to grow in the toxic environment if the first hypothesis is true. If the second, one would expect only a few to survive, and increased survival in future generations.

2   For example, percentage germination, height, dry or fresh mass.

3   a The tolerant plants have grown from seed from the tolerant plants on the waste tip. They survive in competition with normal non-tolerant individuals on normal soil.
  b Non-tolerant plants do not survive in the toxic soil on the tip. Those left will be those which give a high tolerance index when tested.

4   Evidence comes from the percentage germination figures in toxic soil, the higher tolerance index on the tip, and the fairly quick population change at the tip boundaries.

Selection occurs before the plants are seven weeks old, possibly when roots are growing during germination.

5   The direction of the prevailing wind influences the population composition, as *Agrostis* is wind-pollinated and out-breeding. Downwind, tolerant genes are carried into the non-tolerant population, and plants with no tolerance or varying degrees of tolerance survive there equally well. Upwind, there is a flow of non-tolerant genes into tolerant populations, and heavy selection against non-tolerant plants.

6   For example, sea cliffs, hot springs, arctic soil.

6.5   Pesticides

1   a = iii,   b = i,   c = ii.

2   a = 2,   b = 3,   c = 1.